Bust some rhymes in the SATs with CGP!

It can be tricky to get to grips with poetry reading questions, but this CGP SAT Buster is a brilliant way to help pupils gain confidence. It covers all eight reading elements from the KS2 English SATs:

- 2a Word Meanings
- 2b Fact Retrieval
- 2c Summarising
- 2d Inferences
- 2e Predictions
- 2f Structure
- 2g Language
- 2h Comparisons

There are separate question pages for each element, so it's simple for pupils to spot what they're being asked to do. They'll learn how to give exactly the right kind of answer in no time!

What's more, the fun Poetrydactyl tick boxes ask pupils to assess how they're doing, so you'll have an easy way to keep track of their progress.

Published by CGP

Editors: Izzy Bowen, Emma Crighton, Catherine Heygate, Cathy Lear
Reviewer: Samantha Bensted

With thanks to Juliette Green and Sean Walsh for the proofreading.
With thanks to Jan Greenway for the copyright research.

ISBN: 978 1 78294 832 2

Clipart from Corel®
Printed by Elanders Ltd, Newcastle upon Tyne.

Based on the classic CGP style created by Richard Parsons.

Acknowledgements:
p.15: 'Kite Flight'. By kind permission of the Vernon Scannell Literary Estate.
p.33: 'The River's Story' from *Thawing Frozen Frogs* by Brian Patten. Published by Viking Children's Books, 1990. Copyright © Brian Patten. Reproduced by permission of the author c/o Rogers, Coleridge & White Ltd., 20 Powis Mews, London, W11 1JN.

Every effort has been made to locate copyright holders and obtain permission to reproduce sources. For those sources where it has been difficult to trace the originator of the work, we would be grateful for information. If any copyright holder would like us to make an amendment to the acknowledgements, please notify us and we will gladly update the book at the next reprint. Thank you.

Fact Retrieval Questions

Poems can be a bit wordy and complicated, but there are still plenty of cold hard facts to be found. Look at these FACT RETRIEVAL questions and see if you can dig out a few details.

1. Read the first line of the poem.

What causes the dog to look up?

.... **1 mark**

2. While waiting, the dog

barks twice	does not bark	barks once	barks three times

1 mark

Circle your answer.

3. Look at the part of the poem that starts **'He scans the faces...'** and ends **'...by honor he is bound.'**

Write down **two** things the dog is doing while he scans people's faces.

....

.... **2 marks**

4. Which direction does the whistle come from?

.... **1 mark**

5. What does the dog do when he hears the whistle?

trembles	growls	frowns	freezes

1 mark

Circle your answer.

Poetrydactyls love fact retrieval questions more than they love chasing chickens. How did you get on?

Lost Dog

by Frances Rodman

He lifts his hopeful eyes at each new tread,
Dark wells of brown with half his heart in each;
He will not bark, because he is well-bred,
Only one voice can heal the sorry breach*.
He scans the faces that he does not know,
One paw uplifted, ear cocked for a sound
Outside his sight. Only he must not go
Away from here; by honor he is bound.
Now he has heard a whistle down the street;
He trembles in a sort of ecstasy*,
Dances upon his eager, padding feet,
Straining himself to hear, to feel, to see,
And rushes at a call to meet the one
Who of his tiny universe is sun.

breach — gap ecstasy — great happiness

Lost Dog

'Lost Dog' was written by a poet named Frances Rodman. It describes the experiences of a dog who is left alone in a public place. He is surrounded by strangers until he finally hears someone he knows...

What to do —

1) Open out the folding page, and read the poem *Lost Dog*.
2) Then read it again, paying special attention to any tricky bits you didn't understand the first time round.
3) Prepare yourself for battle — dig out your armour and sharpen your sword (or just dig out your rubber and sharpen your pencil). That's it — you're ready to start answering the questions.

Turn the page.

Inference Questions

For INFERENCE questions, you need to think outside the box to work out things that might not be too obvious in the text. Have a go at these questions to test your skills.

1. 'Dark wells of brown with half his heart in each;'

Which part of the dog does this line describe?

ears	eyes	toes	tail

Circle your answer.

1 mark

2. How do you think the dog feels at the end of the poem?

reluctant	upset	tired	excited

Circle your answer.

1 mark

3. 'Who of his tiny universe is sun'

What does this line tell you about the dog's feelings for the person who calls him?

....

1 mark

4. What evidence is there in the poem that the dog is obedient?

Give **two** examples.

....

....

....

2 marks

Poetrydactyls can understand even the trickiest texts. Can you? Tick to show how these pages went.

Word Meaning Questions

Words are the building blocks of any text, so you need to be able to understand what they all mean — even the tricky ones. Try these WORD MEANING questions on for size.

1. **'He lifts his hopeful eyes at each new tread'**

The word **'hopeful'** in this line is closest in meaning to

lucky	**wishful**	**tragic**	**tired**

Circle your answer.

1 mark

2. **'...his eager, padding feet'**

What does the word **'padding'** tell you about the dog's feet? Tick **one** box.

His feet are still. ☐
His feet are moving. ☐
His feet are wet. ☐
His feet are cold. ☐

1 mark

3. **'Straining himself to hear, to feel, to see'**

What does the word **'Straining'** mean in this line?

....

1 mark

4. **'And rushes at a call to meet the one'**

What does the word **'rushes'** tell you about the way the dog moves?

....

1 mark

Poetrydactyls know the meanings of lots of different words. How many do you know?

Summary Questions

When you're answering SUMMARY questions, you have to think about how different parts of the poem work together. Practise summarising by answering these questions.

1. Read the first part of the poem, from the beginning to **'...by honor he is bound.'**

This part of the poem is about

a dog that falls down a well	**a dog that has lost his voice**	**a dog that is waiting for something**	**a dog that has gone blind**

Circle your answer.

1 mark

2. Which of these is a main idea of the whole poem? Tick **one** box.

- Dogs are unfriendly towards strangers. ☐
- Dogs can hear high-pitched whistles. ☐
- You should always keep your dog on a lead. ☐
- Dogs are very loyal animals. ☐

1 mark

2g

Language Question

Poets can be pretty picky about the words they use in their poems, and you need to understand why they've chosen each one. Have a look at this LANGUAGE question.

1. **'Dances upon his eager, padding feet'**

Why do you think the writer chose to use the word **'Dances'** in this line?

....

....

1 mark

Poetrydactyls can answer questions on whole texts and single words in their sleep. How did you get on?

Fact Retrieval Questions

Step one: read poem. Step two: read questions. Step three: find facts. Sounds easy enough, but you still need to practise FACT RETRIEVAL questions — try giving these ones a go.

1. Where in the room is the gentleman in grey's door?

under the table	**beside the mirror**	**in the corner**	**behind the sofa**

Circle your answer.

1 mark

2. Write down **two** things the poem tells you about the eyes of the gentleman in grey.

....

....

2 marks

3. Read the verse that begins **'He swings on the tassels...'**

Write down **three** things the gentleman in grey does in this verse, other than swinging on the tassels.

....

....

....

3 marks

4. Which of these does the gentleman in grey eat in the poem? Tick **two** boxes.

candy crumbs	☐	egg shells	☐	breadcrumbs	☐
apple skins	☐	an apple-seed	☐	a whole cake	☐

1 mark

Poetrydactyls can find facts hidden on an unknown planet in outer space. How about you?

The Gentleman in Grey

Hush, little May! Snuggle here by my side:
Do you see in that corner a door open wide?
That's the door of a house: if you watch it a minute,
The shy little owner will come and sit in it.

See! there he comes; in a grey velvet hat,
With his shining black eyes looking this way and that,
And his velvet-shod* feet: if you stir but a lash,
They'll twinkle and vanish as quick as a flash.

What do you fancy he does in the dark,
When the fire has gone down to the very last spark,
When the girls and the boys are in bed and asleep,
And there's never a cat on the carpet to creep?

Why, out of his doorway he walks at his ease,
And brings his relations and friends, if he please,
He picks up the crumbs of your candy and cake:
From the tiniest fragments a feast he can make.

He swings on the tassels, he climbs up the shelf;
He peeps in the mirror and winks at himself;
He drops from the table, and lands with a thump;
He slides down the sofa, and squeaks at the bump.

There, now he grows bolder; he's out on the floor;
He's eating an apple-seed there by the door;
He's under the table; he's — where did you say?
Oh, here he is! there he is! shoo! get away!

by Emily Huntington Miller

velvet-shod — wearing velvet shoes

The Gentleman in Grey

'The Gentleman in Grey' is a poem written in the nineteenth century by Emily Huntington Miller. It tells the story of a tiny visitor who appears in the narrator's house after dark and makes himself at home.

What to do —

1) Open out the folding page, and read the poem *The Gentleman in Grey.*
2) Check this book for book worms. If you find any, call pest control immediately. If you don't, then it's time to read the poem again to make sure it's all gone in.
3) When you're ready, pick up your pen and start answering the questions.

Turn the page.

Inference Questions

Here's a page of INFERENCE questions for you to try. Remember — for these questions, you'll need to look past the obvious and think about hidden facts and ideas in the poem.

1. Read the first verse of the poem.

Find and copy a phrase that suggests May and the narrator have to wait for the gentleman in grey to appear.

.... **1 mark**

2. Read from **'Why, out of his doorway...'** to **'...squeaks at the bump.'**

In these lines, the gentleman in grey seems

nervous	lonely	angry	confident

1 mark

Circle your answer.

3. What evidence is there to suggest that the narrator is afraid of the gentleman in grey?

....

.... **1 mark**

4. Who or what do you think the gentleman in grey is? Use evidence from the text to explain your answer.

....

....

....

.... **3 marks**

Poetrydactyls can do inference questions while standing on stilts. How did you find them?

Word Meaning Questions

For WORD MEANING questions, you have to prove you understand particular words the writer uses in the text. See how you get on with these word meaning questions.

1. **'And there's never a cat on the carpet to creep'**

   What does the word **'creep'** tell you about the way the cat moves?

   .... **1 mark**

2. Read the verse that begins **'Why, out of his doorway...'**

   What does the word **'feast'** mean in this verse?

   .... **1 mark**

3. **'He peeps in the mirror and winks at himself'**

   Which word could the writer have used in this line to replace **'peeps'**?

squeaks	grins	waves	looks

   Circle your answer. **1 mark**

4. **'There, now he grows bolder; he's out on the floor'**

   What does the word **'bolder'** mean in this line?

weaker	braver	louder	faster

   Circle your answer. **1 mark**

5. Find and copy **two** words from the poem that mean the same as 'thud'.

   ....

   .... **2 marks**

Poetrydactyls are word meaning experts — how did you get on with these questions?

Summary Questions

SUMMARY questions ask you to look at how different bits of the poem fit together, and what the main ideas in the poem are. Read 'The Gentleman in Grey' again, then give these a try.

1. Put these summaries of verses in the order they appear in the poem.

The first one has been done for you.

The narrator wonders what the gentleman in grey does at night.	
The gentleman in grey and his friends eat.	
The gentleman in grey arrives.	
The gentleman in grey explores the room.	
The narrator tells May to watch a door.	1
The narrator finds the gentleman in grey and shoos him away.	

1 mark

2. The title of this poem is **'The Gentleman in Grey'**.

Suggest a different title you could use for the poem.

....

1 mark

2g

Language Question

There's no way around it — you'll need to be able to answer questions about the LANGUAGE of a text in the test. Have a go at this question about 'The Gentleman in Grey'.

1. The writer describes the gentleman in grey's feet as **'velvet-shod'**.

Write down **two** impressions this gives you of his feet.

....

....

2 marks

Poetrydactyls love summary and language questions. Do you? Tick to show how you got on.

Fact Retrieval Questions

For FACT RETRIEVAL questions, make sure you've read the poem really carefully — it can be easy to slip up and make a mistake if you're rushing. Try these questions out.

1. Where does the poem take place?

.... **1 mark**

2. What does the poem tell you about the sky? Tick **one** box.

There are clouds. ☐

It's grey. ☐

It's clear. ☐

There's a rainbow. ☐

1 mark

3. Read from **'It pulls and jerks...'** to **'...towards the trees.'**

Write down **three** animals that the kite is compared to in this part of the poem.

....

....

.... **3 marks**

4. In your own words, describe what happens to the kite in the last two lines of the poem.

....

.... **2 marks**

Poetrydactyls are brilliant at retrieving facts from poems. How did you get on with these questions?

Kite Flight

by Vernon Scannell

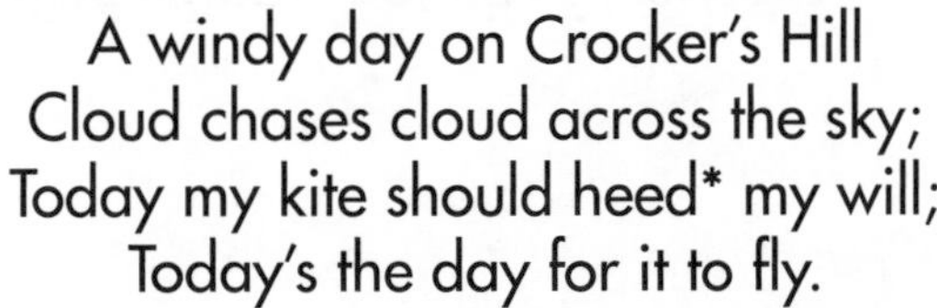

A windy day on Crocker's Hill
Cloud chases cloud across the sky;
Today my kite should heed* my will;
Today's the day for it to fly.

And so it does: it soars up high,
Then briefly dips to rise again,
And I can see its pigtails fly
And feel the tight string's eager strain.

It pulls and jerks as if I held
An eager greyhound on a lead;
A mighty tug and I'm compelled
Almost to see the wild thing freed.

Not quite! I grip with all my might
And think for one mad moment I
Could be dragged upward by my kite
To dangle in astonished sky.

But no, there is a sudden lull;
The wind decides to stand at ease,
And like a swooping hawk or gull
My kite speeds down towards the trees.

Luckily it skims their tops
And arrows back to Crocker's Hill;
It hits the ground, then twitches, flops,
A stranded fish, and then lies still.

* heed — listen to

Kite Flight

If you've ever been outside on a summer's day, watching a kite gliding through the sky, then the events of 'Kite Flight' by Vernon Scannell will feel very familiar. See if you recognise the narrator's experiences as you read through the poem.

What to do —

1) Open out the folding page, and read the poem *Kite Flight*.
2) Then read it through for a second time. Try to focus on anything you found hard to understand at first.
3) Time for a brain break — give yourself a few minutes to digest everything you've read. Then pick up your pen, pencil or goose-feather quill, and get started on the questions.

Turn the page.

Inference Questions

Fact retrieval questions are all fine and dandy, but it's INFERENCE questions that'll have you really digging into what a text means. Try these ones and see how you do.

1. Look at the first verse.

Why does the narrator think it's a good day to fly a kite?

....

1 mark

2. Read the verse that begins **'And so it does...'**

Why is the string **'tight'**? Tick **one** box.

- The kite is falling. ☐
- The string is too short. ☐
- The kite is flying high up. ☐
- There is no wind. ☐

1 mark

3. Read the verse that begins **'It pulls and jerks...'**

How can you tell that the narrator is losing control of the kite?

....

....

1 mark

4. Read the verse that begins **'But no, there is...'**

What makes the kite speed down **'towards the trees'**?

....

....

1 mark

Poetrydactyls are famous for their incredible inference-making skills. How did you find these?

Word Meaning Questions

You know the drill — read through the poem again, then have a look at these WORD MEANING questions. They're all about testing your knowledge of words.

1. **'And so it does: it soars up high'**

   Circle the word which means the same as **'soars'** in this line.

twirls	flies	shudders	crawls

   1 mark

2. **'Then briefly dips to rise again'**

   Which word in this line means 'for a short time'?

   ....

   1 mark

3. **'Not quite! I grip with all my might'**

   What does the word **'might'** mean in this line? Circle your answer.

belief	fingers	string	strength

   1 mark

4. Look at the verse that begins **'But no, there is a sudden lull...'**

   Which word in this verse could be replaced by the word 'diving'?

   ....

   1 mark

5. **'Luckily it skims their tops'**

   What does the word **'skims'** mean in this line?

   ....

   1 mark

Poetrydactyls love word meaning questions — they've learnt the whole Dino Dictionary. How about you?

The last few questions on Kite Flight are under here.

A Night with a Wolf

by James Bayard Taylor (abridged)

High on the lonely mountain
Where the wild men watched and waited;
Wolves in the forest, and bears in the bush,
And I on my path belated*.

The rain and the night together
Came down, and the wind came after,
Bending the props* of the pine tree roof
And snapping many a rafter*.

I crept along in the darkness,
Stunned and bruised and blinded...
Crept to a fir with thick-set boughs,
And a sheltering rock behind it.

There, from the blowing and raining,
Crouching I sought to hide me;
Something rustled, two green eyes shone,
And a wolf lay down beside me.

Little one, be not frightened;
I and the wolf together,
Side by side through the long, long night,
Hid from the awful weather.

His wet fur pressed against me;
Each of us warmed the other;
Each of us felt in the stormy dark
That beast and man were brother.

And when the falling forest
No longer crashed in warning,
Each of us went from our hiding place
Forth in the wild wet morning.

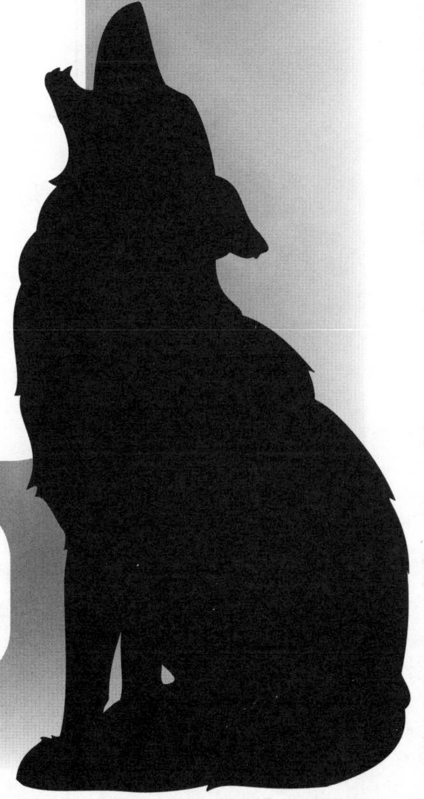

belated — running late
props — supports for a roof
rafter — a beam that supports a roof

A Night with a Wolf

You're stuck outside in a storm and you've finally found some shelter, when a wolf lies down right next to you. Sounds pretty terrifying, if you ask me. That's just what happens to the narrator in James Bayard Taylor's poem 'A Night with a Wolf'...

What to do —

1) Turn over the page, and read the poem *A Night with a Wolf*.
2) Then have a good old read of the poem again. Things are always better the second time round.
3) Now put on your thinking cap. Add a few decorations — mine has big purple feathers and a pom pom on it. Cap ready, get started on the questions.

Turn the page.

Language Questions

LANGUAGE questions are about the words the writer has chosen, and how they're used to describe or explain things in a text. Have a go at these questions to test your skills.

1. **'And arrows back to Crocker's Hill'**

   What does this tell you about the movement of the kite?

   ....

   .... **1 mark**

2. Why do you think the writer chose to describe the kite as a **'stranded fish'** at the end of the poem?

   ....

   .... **1 mark**

2f

Structure Questions

STRUCTURE questions test you on the way a poem has been put together and the order things appear in it. Try out these questions and see how you get on.

1. Read the part of the poem that begins **'Not quite...'** and ends **'...towards the trees.'**

   Find and copy the line where the wind's behaviour changes.

   .... **1 mark**

2. How does the last verse of the poem link back to the first?

   ....

   .... **1 mark**

When it comes to language and structure questions, Poetrydactyls are unbeatable. How did you do?

2b Fact Retrieval Questions

FACT RETRIEVAL questions are about finding information from the text. Read 'A Night with a Wolf' again, then try these questions.

1. Give **one** type of animal mentioned in the poem, other than wolves.

....

1 mark

2. Where does the narrator hide?

up a fir tree	under a pine tree roof	in the wolf's den	under a fir tree by a rock

1 mark

Circle your answer.

3. How do the wolf and the narrator help each other? Tick **one** box.

- They keep each other warm. ☐
- They hide each other from the storm. ☐
- They find food for each other. ☐
- They save each other from an accident. ☐

1 mark

4. At the end of the poem, what do the wolf and the narrator do?

....

....

1 mark

Poetrydactyls use their sharp eyes to spot facts from a mile away. How were these questions for you?

2d

Inference Questions

For INFERENCE questions, you need to think a bit more deeply about what's going on in the poem. Have another look over the poem, then make a start on these questions.

1. Look at the first verse.

   What evidence is there that the mountain might be dangerous? Give **one** example.

   ....

   .... **1 mark**

2. Read the verse that begins **'The rain and...'**

   How can you tell that the wind is strong?

   ....

   .... **1 mark**

3. a) When the wolf lies by him, the narrator seems

scared	calm	hopeless	angry

   1 mark

   Circle your answer.

   b) Explain your answer, making sure you refer to the poem.

   ....

   .... **1 mark**

4. Read from **'There, from the blowing...'** to **'...the awful weather.'**

   Find and copy a line that shows the narrator is telling the story to someone else.

   .... **1 mark**

Once a Poetrydactyl starts doing inference questions, they just can't stop. Tick to show how this page went.

Word Meaning Questions

WORD MEANING questions test you've understood the words from the poem. If you're not sure what a word means, reading the rest of the verse can help you work it out.

1. **'And snapping many a rafter'**

   Circle the word that most closely matches the meaning of **'snapping'**.

   snatching | **hitting** | **breaking** | **crashing**

   1 mark

2. **'Crouching I sought to hide me'**

   Which word in this line means 'tried'?

   ....

   1 mark

3. Look at the verse beginning **'There, from the...'**

   Which word in this verse could be replaced by the word 'gleamed'?

   ....

   1 mark

4. **'Hid from the awful weather'**

   What does the word **'awful'** mean in this line?

   ....

   1 mark

5. Read from **'His wet fur...'** to the end of the poem.

   Find and copy **one** word that means 'animal'.

   ....

   1 mark

Poetrydactyls fly all around the world to learn new word meanings. Did you know the words on this page?

The last few questions on A Night with a Wolf are under here.

Unfold these pages before you start

2b Fact Retrieval Questions

FACT RETRIEVAL questions ask you to — yep — retrieve facts. This means searching the text for the correct information to answer each question.

1. Look at the first verse.

When did it snow? Circle your answer.

during the night	in the morning	at dawn	during the day

1 mark

2. Give **one** thing that the **'young folks'** could hear in their dreams.

1 mark

....

3. Read the verse beginning **'They saw...'**

What is it like outside in this verse? Tick **two** boxes.

It is snowy. ☐ It is warm. ☐

It is foggy. ☐ It is raining. ☐

It is cloudy. ☐ It is sunny. ☐

1 mark

4. Read from **'Out in the clear...'** to the end of the poem.

Put a tick in the correct box to show whether each statement is true or false.

	True	**False**
Kate's feather is scarlet.		
Bess is dancing.		
Joe and Jack are indoors.		
Frank and Tom say hallo.		

1 mark

Poetrydactyls love fact retrieval questions more than they love playing in the snow. How about you?

Summary Question

For SUMMARY questions, you need to understand the overall meanings of the verses in the poem. Check you've grasped the main ideas of 'A Night with a Wolf' by doing this question.

1. Below are summaries of some verses from the poem. Put them in the order they appear in the poem. The first one has been done for you.

The narrator and the wolf find the same hiding place.	☐
The narrator calms the listener's fears.	☐
The narrator explains where the poem takes place.	1
The narrator and the wolf help each other.	☐
The storm arrives.	☐

1 mark

2e

Prediction Question

PREDICTION questions ask you to guess what will happen next. Your answer's got to be based on the poem though — you can't just write about aliens invading for no reason.

1. Do you think that the narrator will go out on the mountain in bad weather again?

Yes ☐ No ☐

Explain your choice fully, using evidence from the text.

....

....

....

....

3 marks

Poetrydactyls are superstars when it comes to summary and prediction questions. How did you do?

Out in the Snow

The world can seem quite magical on snowy days, when the snow turns everything white and makes your everyday surroundings look completely different. 'Out in the Snow' by Louise Chandler Moulton describes this snowy world.

What to do —

1) Turn over the page, and read the poem *Out in the Snow*.
2) Then read it again — this will help you understand any tricky bits.
3) Now imagine building the perfect snowman, carrot and all. Once the snowman's ready in your mind's eye, turn the page and try the questions.

Turn the page.

Out in the Snow

by Louise Chandler Moulton (adapted)

The snow and the silence came down together,
Through the night so white and so still;
And young folks housed from the bitter weather,
Housed from the storm and the chill —

Heard in their dreams the sleigh-bells jingle,
Coasted the hill-sides under the moon,
Felt their cheeks with the keen air tingle,
Skimmed the ice with their steel-clad shoon*.

They saw the snow when they rose in the morning,
Glittering ghosts of the vanished night,
Though the sun shone clear in the winter dawning,
And the day with a frosty pomp* was bright.

Out in the clear, cold, winter weather —
Out in the winter air, like wine —
Kate with her dancing scarlet feather,
Bess with her peacock plumage* fine,

Joe and Jack with their pealing laughter,
Frank and Tom with their glad hallo,
And half a score of roisterers* after,
Out in the witching, wonderful snow,

Shivering graybeards shuffle and stumble,
Righting themselves with a frozen frown,
Grumbling at every snowy tumble;
But young folks know why the snow came down.

steel-clad shoon — shoes with metal attached to them
pomp — a grand display
plumage — feathers
half a score of roisterers — ten people loudly having fun

2d

Inference Questions

You have to act like a detective to answer INFERENCE questions — you need to work out what's going on by using clues in the poem. Test your investigating skills with these questions...

1. Read the verse beginning **'Heard in their...'**

   What does this verse tell you about the young people?

   Tick **one** box.

   They are sleeping out in the snow. ☐

   They want to go out in the snow. ☐

   They don't like playing outside. ☐

   They are too tired to play in the snow. ☐

   1 mark

2. **'Skimmed the ice with their steel-clad shoon'**

   What are the **'young folks'** thinking about in this line? Circle your answer.

   walking | **running** | **ice-skating** | **skipping**

   1 mark

3. How do you think Joe and Jack feel about the snow? Explain your answer.

   ....

   ....

   2 marks

4. What evidence is there in the poem that the **'graybeards'** don't like snow?

   ....

   ....

   ....

   2 marks

Poetrydactyls can do inference questions while sledging downhill with their eyes closed. Can you?

Word Meaning Questions

WORD MEANING questions test your knowledge of elephants. Sorry, I mean words — they test your knowledge of words. Have a go at these questions and see how you get on.

1. **'Housed from the storm and the chill'**

   What does the word **'chill'** mean in this line? Tick **one** box.

   wind ☐

   warmth ☐

   snow ☐

   cold ☐

   1 mark

2. **'Felt their cheeks with the keen air tingle'**

   Which word in this line means the same as 'prickle'?

   ....

   1 mark

3. Read the verse beginning **'They saw...'**

   Which word in this verse could be replaced with the phrase 'got up'?

   ....

   1 mark

4. **'Glittering ghosts of the vanished night'**

   What does the word **'Glittering'** mean in this line?

   ....

   1 mark

Poetrydactyls love word meanings — they read the dictionary every night before bed. How about you?

The last few questions on Out in the Snow are under here.

The River's Story

by Brian Patten

I remember when life was good.
I shilly-shallied across meadows,
Tumbled down mountains,
I laughed and gurgled through woods,
Stretched and yawned in a myriad* of floods.
Insects, weightless as sunbeams,
Settled upon my skin to drink.
I wore lily-pads like medals.
Fish, lazy and battle-scarred,
Gossiped beneath them.
The damselflies were my ballerinas,
The pike* my ambassadors.
Kingfishers, disguised as rainbows,
Were my secret agents.
It was a sweet time, a gone-time,
A time before factories grew,
Brick by greedy brick,
And left me cowering
In monstrous shadows.
Like drunken giants
They vomited their poisons into me.
Tonight a scattering of vagrant bluebells,
Dwarfed by those same poisons,
Toll* my ending.

Children, come and find me if you wish,
I am your inheritance.
Behind the derelict housing-estates
You will discover my remnants.
Clogged with garbage and junk
To an open sewer I've shrunk.

I, who have flowed through history,
Who have seen hamlets become villages,
Villages become towns, towns become cities,
Am reduced to a trickle of filth
Beneath the still, burning stars.

myriad — large number
pike — a type of fish
toll — ring a bell for

The River's Story

In 'The River's Story', a poem by Brian Patten, a river describes its life. It talks about the animals that have lived in and around it, and explains how it has changed over time. It might make you think about the 'story' of a river near you.

What to do —

1) Turn over the page, and read the poem *The River's Story*.
2) Then have another read of the poem. This will help you understand anything that wasn't clear the first time round.
3) Now quickly practise your dancing skills — do a shuffle with your feet and have a boogie with your arms. Then turn over and start the questions.

Turn the page.

Summary Questions

SUMMARY questions ask you to think about ideas from more than one verse in the poem, or even ideas from the whole poem. Get your summarising hat on and do these questions...

1. Read from **'Out in the clear...'** to the end of the poem.

Which phrase best summarises this section of the poem?

Tick **one** box.

- How to keep warm in cold weather ☐
- Different people's experiences of the snow ☐
- Young people going out in the snow ☐
- How to dance in the snow ☐

1 mark

2. Which of these is a main idea in the whole poem?

Snow can be dangerous.	**Young people enjoy the snow.**	**Everyone likes snow.**	**Snow makes everything look nice.**

Circle your answer.

1 mark

2f

Structure Question

For STRUCTURE questions, you need to think about how the poem's been put together, and how different parts of the poem affect its meaning as a whole. Give this question a try...

1. How does the last verse of the poem link back to the first verse?

....

....

1 mark

Poetrydactyls do summary and structure questions in the blink of an eye. How did you get on?

Fact Retrieval Questions

2b

The information you need for FACT RETRIEVAL questions will always be there in the poem. You just need to read it closely until you spot what you're after.

1. Look at the first verse. Give **one** place through which the river flowed.

.... **1 mark**

2. Why did **'Insects'** land on the river?

.... **1 mark**

3. Draw lines to match the animals to their roles.

damselflies	**secret agents**
pike	**ballerinas**
kingfishers	**ambassadors**

1 mark

4. What were the factories made from?

.... **1 mark**

5. Read the verse beginning **'Children, come and find me...'**

Where are the river's **'remnants'**?

.... **1 mark**

Poetrydactyls use their beaks to snap up even the trickiest of facts. How did you find these questions?

2d

Inference Questions

o do INFERENCE questions, you need to be like a scuba diver — you have to dive into the oem to find the deeper meanings. Read the poem again, then try answering these questions.

. How do you think the river felt before the factories grew?

Explain your answer using evidence from the text.

....

.... **2 marks**

2. Find and copy a phrase that suggests the kingfishers were colourful.

.... **1 mark**

3. **'And left me cowering'**

How does this line make the reader feel about the river?

.... **1 mark**

4. Read from **'A time before factories...'** to **'...their poisons into me.'**

What impressions do you get of the factories from this section?

Support your answer with evidence from the text.

....

....

....

.... **3 marks**

Poetrydactyls think inference questions are more fun than bouncing on a trampoline. How did you get on?

Word Meaning Questions

Have you ever wanted to feel cleverer than a parrot? Now's your chance — for WORD MEANING questions, you've got to say what words mean, not just repeat them again and again (squawk).

1. **'Tumbled down mountains'**

   What does the word **'Tumbled'** mean in this line?

   .... 1 mark

2. Look at the first verse.

   Find and copy **one** word from this verse that means 'chatted'.

   .... 1 mark

3. Read the second verse.

   Find and copy **one** word from this verse that means 'desire'.

   .... 1 mark

4. **'Clogged with garbage and junk'**

   What does the word **'Clogged'** mean in this line?

   .... 1 mark

5. Look at the last verse.

   What does the word **'trickle'** suggest about the river's size?

   .... 1 mark

Poetrydactyls can do word meaning questions while flying upside down. How did you find this page?